Play Ball!

All I Ever Learned I Forgot
by the Third Inning

by Jeff MacNelly

TRIUMPH
BOOKS

CHICAGO

Printed in the United States

This book is available in quantity at special discounts
for your group or organization. For more information, contact:

Triumph Books
601 South LaSalle Street
Chicago, Illinois 60605
(312) 939-3330 Fax (312) 663-3557

Book design and typesetting by Sue Knopf.
Cover design by James Baran.

ISBN 1-57243-328-0

Play Ball!

I HAVE THE IMPOSING PRESENCE ON THE MOUND OF A RICK SUTCLIFFE.

I'VE GOT THE CONFIDENCE OF A NOLAN RYAN

AND A WINDUP LIKE BRET SABERHAGEN.

NOT TO MENTION SUPERIOR BASEBALL SMARTS LIKE OREL HERSHISER.

SO WHAT'S MY PROBLEM?

YOU GOT THE DELIVERY OF A MARVIN BLIGGINS.

WHO'S HE?

MY PAPER BOY.

3

4

By Jeff MacNelly

HEY, IRVING... I GOT AN EXTRA TICKET TO TODAY'S CUBS GAME. —WANNA COME?

SURE!

LET ME CHECK WITH THE WIFE.

HONEY? IS IT OKAY IF I GO TO THE CUBS GAME WITH PERFESSER?

SIGH

SHE SAYS I CAN GO.

AH, MARRIAGE!

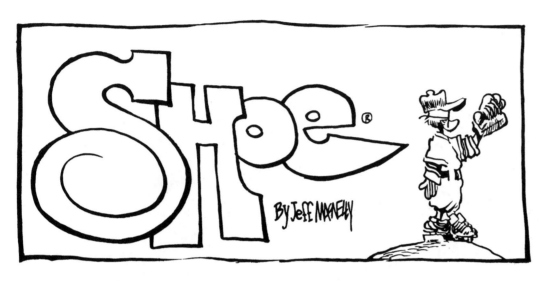

AARRGH!! WHAP!

I HATE CATCHERS WHO THROW HARDER THAN I CAN.

RIGHT, MOOSE, I KNOW... I GOT THE SIGNALS...

SIGH CATCHERS AND THEIR MEETINGS...

HERE GOES...

UMPH...

BALL FOUR!!

WHAT IS IT THIS TIME, MOOSE?

JUST ONE QUESTION...

DO YOU SINCERELY WANT TO BE A DECENT PITCHER?

OH NO.

ANOTHER ONE OF HIS MOTIVATIONAL SEMINARS...

DARE TO THROW HEAT ON A 3-0

17

NICE PITCH.

THANKS, BUT WHAT DOES "HOOIPE" MEAN?...

THAT'S UMPIRESE FOR "STRIKE."

OH. THEN I ASSUME THAT "HAWP" IS A BALL.

RIGHT.

EXCEPT IF IT'S FOLLOWED BY A STREAM OF TOBACCO JUICE.

25

26

SHoe By Jeff MacNelly

WE CAN'T GO ON MEETING LIKE THIS.

WHY NOT?

PEOPLE ARE BEGINNING TO TALK.

THEY'RE STARTING TO THINK SOME OF THESE RIDICULOUS PITCHES YOU'VE BEEN MAKING ARE MY IDEA...

ABOUT THE NEXT HITTER...

HITTER?

YEAH, THE HITTER WHO'S UP NEXT.

WHY DO YOU CALL HIM "HITTER"?

29

THERE YOU ARE, THE AGING VETERAN, WONDERING IF YOU STILL HAVE IT.

YOU WONDER IF YOU CAN GET YOUR BODY IN SHAPE FOR YET ANOTHER SUMMER CAMPAIGN.

SO YOU GO TO SPRING TRAINING TO TUNE YOUR BODY, TO HONE YOUR SKILLS, REBUILD YOUR STAMINA ...

TO FIND OUT IF YOU STILL HAVE ENOUGH OF THE OLD MOVES...

TO SEE IF YOU STILL HAVE ONE MORE SEASON LEFT IN YOU...

YUP. LOOKS LIKE I MADE THE CUT AGAIN THIS YEAR...

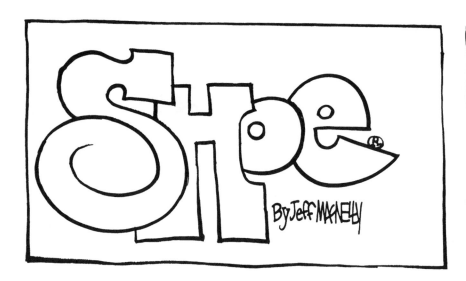

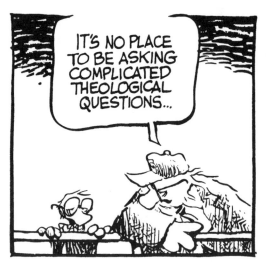

I'VE HEARD OF THE SEVENTH-INNING STRETCH...

BUT WHAT'S THIS FOURTH-INNING STUFF?

IT'S A TRADITION IN WRIGLEY FIELD...

WHEN YOU COME HERE TO A BALLGAME ON A WEEKDAY AFTERNOON,

YOU NEED THE FOURTH-INNING STRETCH...

TO THINK UP SOME EXCUSE...

AND CALL YOUR OFFICE.

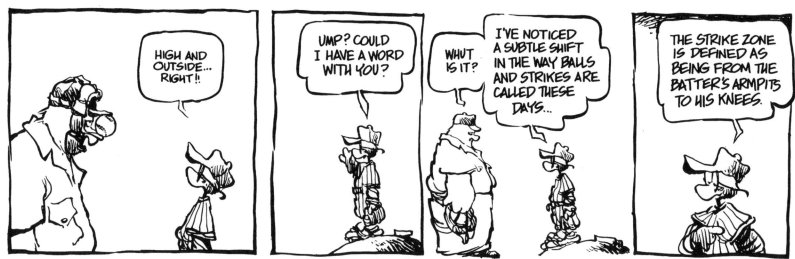

SOAK UP SOME RAYS...

MAYBE A FEW BREWS...

OF COURSE, I HAVE TO MAKE SURE NO ONE RECOGNIZES ME...

GATE 9

SO I TAKE THE USUAL PRECAUTIONS.

CAN'T HAVE PEOPLE FINDING ME OUT HERE ON COMPANY TIME...

MACNELLY

43

45

GO OVER TO THE VACANT LOTS, PICK UP TEAMS, AND PLAY.

GEE, I DON'T KNOW. IT SOUNDS SORT OF UNORGANIZED.

EXACTLY. WE DON'T NEED UNIFORMS, CARPOOLS, PARENTS, CHEERLEADERS...

WE'RE JUST KIDS PLAYING BASEBALL IN A VACANT LOT— JUST LIKE IN THE OLD DAYS...

YOU CAN BE CATCHER!!

OKAY, BUT I HAVE TO WARN YOU...

MY AGENT WILL ASK FOR ABOUT 2.3 MILLION.

HEY!! I HIT .238 LAST SEASON!!!

TAKE ME OUT TO THE BALLLL GAME!!...

TAKE ME OUT TO THE CROWWWD...

BUY ME SOME PEANUTS AND CRACKER JACK...

I DON'T CARE IF WE NEVER GET BACK...

54

IS THERE ANYTHING IN THE WORLD BETTER THAN PLAYING BASEBALL?

Shoe

By Jeff MacNelly

YEAH. WATCHING SOMEONE ELSE PLAY BASEBALL.

HAVE YOU EVER NOTICED HOW BALLPARKS ARE A LOT LIKE THEIR CITIES?...

FENWAY PARK IS OLD, SORTA LOPSIDED AND RAUCOUS—JUST LIKE BOSTON.

THEN THERE'S YANKEE STADIUM.

IT'S HUGE, AWESOME AND EXPENSIVE— JUST LIKE THE BIG APPLE.

AND LOOK AT WRIGLEY FIELD... IT'S SOLID, WORKMANLIKE, WITH A NEIGHBORHOOD FLAVOR THAT JUST SAYS "CHICAGO."

YOU CAN FIND OUT A LOT ABOUT A CITY BY GOING TO THE LOCAL BALLPARK.

LIKE THE TREEDOME HERE. WE PLAY A UNIQUE BRAND OF BASEBALL IN COLORFUL SURROUNDINGS...

WHICH TELLS A LOT ABOUT US AS A COMMUNITY...

RIGHT.

ESPECIALLY WHEN WE USE THE WINO FOR THIRD BASE.

MacNELLY

57

NOW WE'RE GETTING SOMEWHERE.

MAYBE...

BUT LET'S KEEP OUR PERSPECTIVE.

WHILE THE SINGLE WAS A REFRESHING CHANGE OF PACE FROM THE HOME RUNS, DON'T GET A BIG HEAD.

YOUR CURVE BALL ISN'T CURVING.

YOUR SLIDER ISN'T SLIDING.

YOUR FASTBALL, HOWEVER, DOES LOOK LIKE IT'S BEEN FASTING.

.. BUT HEAD FOR THE BALLPARK.

I GUESS I'M JUST A BASEBALL FREAK...

I ALWAYS GET HERE VERY EARLY.

— WAY BEFORE BATTING PRACTICE —

SO I CAN WATCH THE AGENTS WARM UP.

GET SERIOUS!! MY CLIENT HAS A LIFETIME .282, PAL...

JUST LOOK AT HIS TOTAL BASES!! COMPARE THAT TO ANY OTHER CATCHER!!

BUT NOW THAT HE'S HAD THE OPERATION...

I DON'T THINK WE CAN EVEN THINK DEAL HERE.

MACNELLY

THE BALLPARKS ARE SMALLER AND MORE INTIMATE THAN THE BIG CITY STADIUMS,

THE WEATHER IS GREAT,

AND THERE ISN'T A LOUSY SEAT IN THE WHOLE PLACE.

SO YOU'RE CLOSER TO THE ACTION.

—WHICH IS GREAT FOR THE FANS.

.. AND NOT SO GREAT FOR THE GAME...

NOW WATCH THE MOVEMENT HE GETS ON HIS SPLIT-FINGER FASTBALL .... SEE? ...HE'S SCUFFING THE BALL !!

LIGHTS IN WRIGLEY FIELD WILL MEAN FEWER GAMES PLAYED IN THE SUNSHINE.

OH NO.

DOES THAT MEAN THE IVY WILL DIE?

WHAT'S THE BULLHORN FOR, SKYLER?

I'M DOING A SURVEY.

I WANT TO FIND OUT HOW THE FANS HERE AT WRIGLEY REALLY FEEL...

ABOUT ONE OF THE GREAT PHILOSOPHICAL DEBATES OF OUR TIME:

WHETHER OR NOT THERE SHOULD BE LIGHTS INSTALLED HERE IN THE LAST BASTION OF DAY BASEBALL.

I'M AFRAID THAT'S AN ISSUE THAT WILL NEVER BE SETTLED.

WELL, THERE'S ONLY ONE WAY TO FIND OUT...

ATTENTION, CUB FANS!!

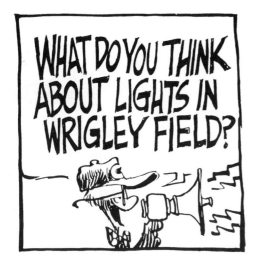

WHAT DO YOU THINK ABOUT LIGHTS IN WRIGLEY FIELD?

LESS FILLING

MAYBE I SHOULD HAVE WORDED IT DIFFERENTLY...

TASTES GREAT!!

MACNELLY

HEY HOT DOG! BEER HERE

THE SHOUTS OF THE VENDORS...

WHAPP!

THE SLAP OF THE BALL IN THE GLOVE...

HAWPTEW!

THE UMPIRE CALLING BALLS...

HEEIPE!

— AND STRIKES.

OH YEAH? MAKE ME!

AND THAT, OF COURSE...

WHAT WAS THAT?

THE WHINE OF THE OVERPAYED PLAYER.

MACNELLY

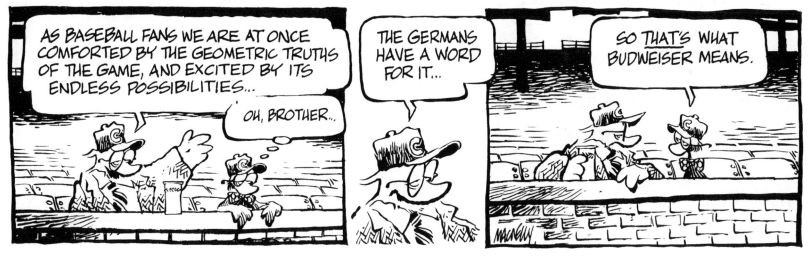

83

Mets Murder Giants, 17-2.

Cubs Demolish St. Louis, 14-2.

Padres Rip Guts Out of LA, 15-0.

Rangers Eaten Alive By Indians, 13-0.

?

Pirates Quite Rude to Atlanta, 4-1.

WHAT THE HECK, IT'S JUST A GAME.

89

WILL THE PITCHING IMPROVE? WILL THE NEW GUYS BLEND INTO THE LINE-UP?

HOW'S THE BULLPEN?... WILL WE BE PLAGUED BY INJURIES?

THEN, OF COURSE, WHAT ABOUT THE VETERANS?

DO THEY STILL HAVE THE TOOLS TO MAKE IT THROUGH ONE MORE SEASON?

LET'S SEE...

SCORECARD, PENCIL, SUNTAN OIL, HOT DOG, BASEBALL HAT, SOFT PRETZEL, BEER...

YUP, YOU STILL GOT ALL THE TOOLS...

THAT'S YOUR EARNED RUN AVERAGE.

OKAY, BUT WHAT DOES THAT MEAN?

WELL, YOUR ERA. IS, WHAT, 22.90?...

YEAH, BUT 22.90 <u>WHAT</u>?

HMM...

WELL, I THINK THEY TAKE ALL THE RUNS YOU'VE GIVEN UP SO FAR THIS YEAR...

THEN THEY MEASURE THEM...

IN MILES.

MACNELLY.

99

By Jeff Macnelly

BALL FOUR!!

GOOD GRAVY!

THINGS JUST CAN'T GET WORSE THAN THIS.

BALL FIVE!!

NOTHING'S WORKING...

WELL, HANG IN THERE.

I'VE WALKED FIVE GUYS IN A ROW!!

I'M MISSING WITH THE CURVE...

I CAN'T GET THE FASTBALL ACROSS...

YOU'VE GOT YOUR STUFF...

BUT YOU CAN'T <u>BUY</u> A STRIKE.

IT'S THE UMP— HE WON'T GIVE ME A BREAK...

I THINK HE'S BEEN MESSING WITH THE STRIKE ZONE.

YOU THINK IT'S SMALLER?...

NO, JUST A LOT FARTHER...

101

BASEBALL IS A CEREBRAL GAME.

HUH?

THAT MEANS BASEBALL IS A GAME WHERE YOU HAVE TO USE YOUR HEAD.

LOOK AT THE MANAGER THERE, FOR INSTANCE.

THERE'S A LOT GOING ON INSIDE HIS HEAD.

RIGHT.

BUT A LOT OF IT ENDS UP ON THE DUGOUT FLOOR.

PTOOEY!

O'ER THE
LA·A·AND OF
THE F·R·EE·EE!..

I HATE THESE ROAD GAMES IN ATLANTA...

AND THE HOME OF THE

I GUESS IT'S THEIR FIGHT SONG~

...*Braves!*

IT'S SORT OF PRETENTIOUS.

MACNELLY.

WHAT DO YOU DO WITH ALL THESE BASEBALL CARDS, PERFESSER?... COLLECT 'EM?...

NAH.

STORE

I'M TOO OLD FOR ALL THAT NONSENSE...

I CLIP 'EM TO MY BICYCLE.

WHAP WHAP WHAP

MACNELLY.